TWENTY CLASSIC CHRISTMAS CAROLS

Words and Music

BLACKTHORN PRESS

Blackthorn Press, Blackthorn House
Middleton Rd, Pickering, YO18 8AL
United Kingdom

www.blackthornpress.com

ISBN 978-1-906259-11-2

All rights reserved. No part of this publication may be
reproduced, stored in a retrieval system or transmitted,
in any form or by any means, electronic, mechanical,
photocopying, recording, or otherwise, without the
prior permission of the Blackthorn Press.

Printed and bound in Great Britain by
CPI Antony Rowe, Chippenham and Eastbourne

INTRODUCTION

As With Gladness, Men of Old

On the day of the Epiphany 1860, while sick in bed, William C Dix wrote the words of this hymn. It was first published in Dix' *Hymns of Love and Joy*. The original tune was composed by Conrad Kocher in 1838 and was adapted by Dix and William Henry Monk.

| *William Chatterton Dix* | *Conrad Kocher* | *William James Kirkpatrick* |
| *(1837-1898)* | *(1786-1872)* | *(1838-1921)* |

Away in a Manger

This carol was first published in an 1885 Lutheran Sunday school book by James R Murray. There are two well known melodies for the carol: 'Cradle Song', more commonly used in the United Kingdom and 'Mueller', more commonly found in the United States. The tune predominantly used in the United Kingdom was written by William J Kirkpatrick and was first published in 1895. The third stanza was added in 1904 by John McFarland of New York City, although it is unclear if he penned it himself. The author of the first two stanzas is unknown.

Deck the Halls

J P McCaskey is sometimes credited with the lyrics of Deck the Halls but he only edited the *Franklin Square Song Collection* in which the lyrics were first published in 1881. The author is unknown but the words are said to originate in America. In 1788 Mozart used the tune in his Sonata in G for violin and keyboard. The earliest existing source of the melody, 'Nos Galen', was found in a manuscript compiled by Welsh harpist John Dall (1710-1782). In Wales today the tune is attached to a text known as "Oer Yw'r Gwr" (Cold is the Man) that deals with New Year's Eve celebrations.

Ding Dong Merrily on High

The composer of this carol is unknown, but it is reputed to be French in origin. It first appeared in print in 1588 in the *Orchésographie*, a dance book written by catholic priest Jehan Tabourot. It first emerged in its current form in 1924 with words by George Ratcliffe Woodward, collaborating with Charles Wood, in the *Cambridge Carol-Book: Being Fifty-two Songs for Christmas, Easter, And Other Seasons*. Ding Dong Merrily on High was originally in Latin - 'Gloria in Excelsis Deo'.

The First Noel

This carol is of unknown origin, but generally thought to be 16th century English. There is a misconception that the carol is French in origin due to the French spelling of Noel as opposed to the Anglo-Saxon spelling of the word as Nowell. The early printed versions of this carol use the Nowell or Nowel spelling, it first being published in *Christmas Carols Ancient and Modern* in 1833.

God Rest Ye Merry, Gentlemen

Sung for centuries before being published in 1833, when it appeared in *Christmas Carols Ancient and Modern*, a collection of seasonal carols gathered by William B Sandys.

Good King Wenceslas

The lyrics of this carol are by John Mason Neale. The tune is that of 'Tempus Adest Floridum' ('It is Time for Flowering'), a 13th century spring carol, first published in the Swedish *Piae Cantiones* in 1582. Rev Neale translated many of the carols and hymns from this volume and together with Rev Thomas Helmore produced 12 carols for *Carols for Christmas-Tide* in 1853.

John Mason Neale
(1818-1866)

Charles Wesley
(1707-1788)

Felix Mendelssohn
(1809-1847)

Hark! The Herald Angels Sing

First appearing in *Hymns and Sacred Poems* in 1739, it was written by Charles Wesley and sung to a different tune than the one preferred today. Just over a hundred years later Felix Mendelssohn composed a cantata in 1840 to commemorate Johann Gutenberg's invention of the printing press. William H Cummings then adapted Mendelssohn's music to fit the lyrics, which had by that time been altered by various hands, most notably George Whitefield who gave us the familiar opening line.

The Holly and the Ivy

Holly and Ivy have for centuries been taken indoors during the winter and have been a mainstay of Christmas decoration for church use since around the fifteenth or sixteenth centuries. The colours of holly and ivy, green and red are traditionally associated with Christmas. The author and composer of the Holly and the Ivy are unknown. The music and some of the text were collected by Cecil Sharp from a woman in Chipping Campden, Gloucestershire. This carol is probably related to an older carol 'The Contest of the Ivy and the Holly', a contest between the traditional emblems of woman and man respectively.

In the Bleak Midwinter

Written by English poet Christina Rossetti around 1872 and published posthumously in Rossetti's *Poetic Works* in 1904. It became a Christmas carol after it appeared in *The English Hymnal* in 1906 with a setting by Gustav Holst.

Portait of Chistina Rossetti (1830-1894) by her brother Dante Gabriel Rossetti

Gustav Holst (1874-1934) by Herbert Lambert, 1923

I Saw Three Ships

Believed to be an English carol from the Victorian era, the author or authors are unknown. Some sources assert that this song is an upbeat variant of 'Greensleeves', which has a similar meter. The earliest printed version is from the 17th century.

It Came Upon the Midnight Clear

This poem and Christmas carol written by Edmund Sears, pastor of the Unitarian Church in Weston, Massachusetts in 1849 and first appeared in the *Christian Register* in Boston. In 1850 Richard Storrs Willis, a composer who trained under Felix Mendelssohn, wrote the melody called 'Carol'. 'Carol' is the most widely known tune to the song in the United States. In the United Kingdom the tune called 'Noel', which was adapted from an English melody in 1874 by Arthur Sullivan, is the usual accompaniment.

Arthur Seymour Sullivan
(1842-1900)

Lowell Mason
(1792-1872)

Joy to the World

The scripture based words are by Isaac Watts. The music was adapted and arranged by Lowell Mason in 1839 from an older melody most probably originating from Handel. Two musical phrases from Handel's Messiah 'Lift up your heads' and 'Comfort Ye' have clearly been woven into the melody we still use today.

O Come, All Ye Faithful

Circa 1743 John F Wade wrote 'Adeste Fideles' with four Latin verses that in 1841 were translated into English by Frederick Oakeley. Additional verses were translated by William T Brooke.

O Come, O Come Emmanuel

Written in Latin in the 12th century by author or authors unknown, it is believed that the melody was of French origin and added to the text around a hundred years later. The Latin was translated into English by John Mason Neale and published in *Mediaeval Hymns*, 1851.

Phillips Brooks
(1835-1893)

John Henry Hopkins Jr.
(1820-1891)

Franz Xaver Gruber
(1787-1863)

O Little Town of Bethlehem

Phillips Brooks, an episcopal priest in Philadelphia, was inspired when visiting the town of Bethlehem in 1865 where he assisted with the midnight service on Christmas Eve. Three years later he wrote the poem for his church. His organist, Lewis Redner, added the music, 'St. Louis', which remains the tune most often used for this carol in the United States. The English tune 'Forest Green', adapted by Ralph Vaughan Williams in 1906, is the tune most often used for this carol in the United Kingdom.

Silent Night

The original lyrics of the song 'Stille Nacht' were written in German by the Austrian priest Father Josef Mohr and the melody was composed by the Austrian headmaster Franz Xaver Gruber. The version of the melody that is generally sung today differs slightly (particularly in the final strain) from Gruber's original.

The carol was first performed in the Nicola-Kirche (Church of St. Nicholas) in Oberndorf, Austria on December 24, 1818. Mohr had composed the words a few years earlier, in 1816, but on Christmas Eve brought them to Gruber and asked him to compose a melody and guitar accompaniment for the church service.

The song was sung simultaneously in English and German by troops during the Christmas truce of 1914, as it was one of the few carols that soldiers on both sides of the front line knew.

We Three Kings of Orient Are

Originally published in 1863 by John Hopkins Jr. in his *Carols, Hymns, and Songs* it began life with the title 'Three Kings of Orient'.

We Wish You a Merry Christmas

Believed to come from the West Country of England in the 16th century.

While Shepherds Watched Their Flocks

The lyrics are attributed to Nahum Tate although the exact date of Tate's composition is unknown. The words appeared in Tate and Nicholas Brady's 1700 supplement to their psalter, *New Version of the Psalms of David* of 1696.

The hymn tune 'Cranbrook' was written for the words in 1805 by Canterbury shoe-maker Thomas Clark and is now better known in the United Kingdom as the tune of 'On Ilkla Moor Baht 'at'. The melody most commonly used in the United Sates was arranged by Lowell Mason in 1821. In the United Kingdom and Canada the standard arrangement of the music 'Old Winchester' is originally from Este's psalter, the *Whole Book of Psalmes*, from 1592, but arranged by William Henry Monk sometime before 1874.

William Henry Monk
(1823-1889)

CONTENTS

As with glad - ness, men of old Did the guid - ing star be - hold

As with joy they hailed its light Lead - ing on - ward, beam - ing bright

So, most glor - ious Lord, may we Ev - er - more be led to Thee.

As With Gladness Men of Old

1. As with gladness men of old, Did the guiding star behold
As with joy they hailed its light
Leading onward, beaming bright
So, most glorious Lord, may we
Evermore be led to Thee

2. As with joyful steps they sped, To that lowly manger bed
There to bend the knee before
Him Whom heaven and earth adore
So may we with willing feet
Ever seek Thy mercy seat

3. As they offered gifts most rare, At that manger rude and bare
So may we with holy joy
Pure and free from sin's alloy
All our costliest treasures bring
Christ, to Thee, our heavenly King

4. Holy Jesus, every day, Keep us in the narrow way
And, when earthly things are past
Bring our ransomed souls at last
Where they need no star to guide
Where no clouds Thy glory hide

5. In the heavenly country bright, Need they no created light
Thou its light, its joy, its crown
Thou its sun which goes not down
There forever may we sing
Alleluias to our King

F   Gm/C   F   Am

A - way in a— man - ger, no— crib for a

Gm   Gm7   C7/E   C   F   Dm   G/B   G7

bed, The— lit - tle Lord Je - sus laid— down His sweet

C   C7   F   Gm/F   F   Am

head. The stars in the— bright sky looked down where He

Gm   Gm7   C7/E   C   F   Dm   Gm/B♭   C7   F

lay, The— lit - tle Lord Je - sus, a - sleep on the hay.

2

Away in a Manger

Away in a manger, no crib for a bed
The little Lord Jesus laid down His sweet head
The stars in the bright sky looked down where He lay
The little Lord Jesus, asleep on the hay

The cattle are lowing, the baby awakes
But little Lord Jesus, no crying He makes
I love Thee, Lord Jesus, look down from the sky
And stay by my side, until morning is nigh

Be near me, Lord Jesus, I ask Thee to stay
Close by me forever, and love me, I pray
Bless all the dear children in Thy tender care
And take us to heaven to live with Thee there

Deck the halls with boughs of hol - ly, fa la la la la la la la la.

'Tis the sea - son to be jol - ly, fa la la la la la la la la.

Don we now our gay ap - par - el, fa la la la la la la la la.

Toll the an - cient Yule - tide car - ol, fa la la la la la la la la.

Deck the Halls

Deck the halls with boughs of holly
Fa la la la la, la la la la
'Tis the season to be jolly
Fa la la la la, la la la la
Don we now our gay apparel
Fa la la, la la la, la la la
Toll the ancient Yuletide carol
Fa la la la la, la la la la
See the blazing Yule before us
Fa la la la la, la la la la
Strike the harp and join the chorus
Fa la la la la, la la la la
Follow me in merry measure
Fa la la, la la la, la la la
While I tell of Yuletide treasure
Fa la la la la, la la la la
Fast away the old year passes
Fa la la la la, la la la la
Hail the new, ye lads and lasses
Fa la la la la, la la la la
Sing we joyous, all together
Fa la la, la la la, la la la
Heedless of the wind and weather
Fa la la la la, la la la la

Ding dong! Mer - ri - ly on high in heav'n the bells are ring - ing Ding dong! Ve - ri - ly the sky is riv'n with an - gel sing - ing Glo - - - - - - - - - o - - - - - ri - a, ho - san - na in ex - cel - sis!

Ding Dong Merrily on High

Ding dong! Merrily on high
In heav'n the bells are ringing
Ding dong! Verily the sky
Is riv'n with angel singing
Gloria, hosanna in excelsis!
Gloria, hosanna in excelsis!

E'en so here below, below
Let steeple bells be swungen
And "Io, io, io!"
By priest and people sungen
Gloria, hosanna in excelsis!
Gloria, hosanna in excelsis!

Pray you, dutifully prime
Your matin chime, ye ringers
May you beautifully rime
Your evetime song, ye singers
Gloria, hosanna in excelsis!
Gloria, hosanna in excelsis!

The First Noel

1. The first noel, the angel did say
Was to certain poor shepherds in fields as they lay
In fields where they lay keeping their sheep
On a cold winter's night that was so deep
Noel, Noel, Noel, Noel
Born is the King of Israel

2. They looked up and saw a star
Shining in the east, beyond them far
And to the earth it gave great light
And so it continued both day and night

3. And by the light of that same star
Three wise men came from country far
To seek for a King was their intent
And to follow the star wherever it went

4. This star drew nigh to the northwest
O'er Bethlehem it took its rest
And there it did both stop and stay
Right o'er the place where Jesus lay

5. Then entered in those wise men three
Full reverently upon their knee
And offered there in His presence
Their gold and myrrh and frankincense

6. Then let us all with one accord
Sing praises to our heavenly Lord
That hath made heaven and earth of naught
And with His blood mankind has bought

God rest ye mer - ry, gen - tle-men, let noth - ing you dis - may, re-

mem-ber Christ our Sav - iour was born on Christ-mas day to save us all from

Sa - tan's power when we were gone a - stray. O ti - dings of com - fort and

joy, com - fort and joy, O ti - dings of com - fort and joy!

God Rest Ye Merry, Gentlemen

1. God rest ye merry, gentlemen, let nothing you dismay
Remember, Christ our Saviour was born on Christmas day
To save us all from Satan's power when we were gone astray
O tidings of comfort and joy, Comfort and joy
O tidings of comfort and joy

2. In Bethlehem, in Israel, this blessed Babe was born
And laid within a manger upon this blessed morn
The which His mother Mary did nothing take in scorn

3. From God our heavenly Father a blessed angel came
And unto certain shepherds brought tidings of the same
How that in Bethlehem was born the Son of God by name

4. "Fear not then," said the angel, "Let nothing you affright
This day is born a Saviour of a pure virgin bright
To free all those who trust in Him from Satan's power and might"

5. The shepherds at those tidings rejoiced much in mind
And left their flocks a-feeding in tempest, storm and wind
And went to Bethl'em straightaway this blessed Babe to find

6. And when they came to Bethlehem where our dear Saviour lay
They found Him in a manger where oxen feed on hay
His mother Mary kneeling down unto the Lord did pray

7. Now to the Lord sing praises all you within this place
And with true love and brotherhood each other now embrace
This holy tide of Christmas all others doth deface

11

Good King Wen - ces - las looked out on the Feast of Ste - phen

when the snow lay round a - bout, deep and crisp and e - ven.

Bright - ly shone the moon that night, though the frost was cru - el,

when a poor man came in sight, gath - 'ring win - ter fu - - - el.

Good King Wenceslas

1. Good King Wenceslas looked out on the feast of Stephen
When the snow lay round about, deep and crisp and even
Brightly shone the moon that night, though the frost was cruel
When a poor man came in sight, gath'ring winter fuel

2. "Hither, page, and stand by me, if thou know'st it, telling
Yonder peasant, who is he? Where and what his dwelling?"
"Sire, he lives a good league hence, underneath the mountain
Right against the forest fence, by Saint Agnes' fountain"

3. "Bring me flesh and bring me wine, bring me pine logs hither
You and I will see him dine, when we bear him thither"
Page and monarch, forth they went, forth they went together
Through the rude wind's wild lament and the bitter weather

4. "Sire, the night is darker now, and the wind blows stronger
Fails my heart, I know not how; I can go no longer"
"Mark my footsteps, my good page, tread thou in them boldly
You shall find the winter's rage freeze thy blood less coldly"

5. In his master's steps he trod, where the snow lay dinted
Heat was in the very sod which the Saint had printed
Therefore, christian men, be sure, wealth or rank possessing
Ye who now will bless the poor shall yourselves find blessing

Hark! The her - ald an - gels sing, "Glo - ry to the new - born King;

peace on earth and mer - cy mild, God and sin - ners rec - on - ciled!"

Joy - ful, all ye na - tions, rise, join the tri - umph of the skies;

with th'an - gel - ic host pro-claim, "Christ is born in Beth - le - hem!"

Hark! The her - ald an - gels sing, "Glo - ry to the new - born King!"

Hark! The Herald Angels Sing

Hark! The herald angels sing
Glory to the newborn King!
Peace on earth, and mercy mild
God and sinners reconciled
Joyful, all ye nations rise
Join the triumph of the skies
With th'angelic host proclaim
Christ is born in Bethlehem
Hark! The herald angels sing
Glory to the newborn King!

Christ, by highest heav'n adored
Christ the everlasting Lord
Late in time behold Him come
Offspring of a virgin's womb
Veiled in flesh the Godhead see
Hail th'incarnate Deity
Pleased as man with man to dwell
Jesus, our Emmanuel

Hail the heav'n-born Prince of Peace!
Hail the Sun of Righteousness!
Light and life to all He brings
Ris'n with healing in His wings
Mild He lays His glory by
Born that man no more may die
Born to raise the sons of earth
Born to give them second birth

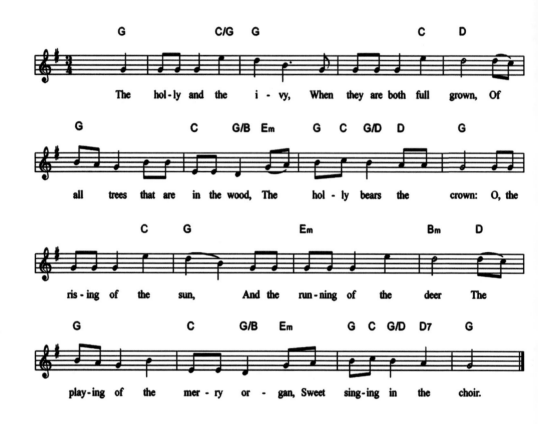

The hol-ly and the i - vy, When they are both full grown, Of all trees that are in the wood, The hol - ly bears the crown: O, the ris - ing of the sun, And the run - ning of the deer The play-ing of the mer - ry or - gan, Sweet sing-ing in the choir.

The Holly and the Ivy

1. The holly and the ivy
When they are both full grown
Of all trees that are in the wood
The holly bears the crown
O, the rising of the sun
And the running of the deer
The playing of the merry organ
Sweet singing in the choir

2. The holly bears a blossom
As white as lily flow'r
And Mary bore sweet Jesus Christ
To be our dear Saviour

3. The holly bears a berry
As red as any blood
And Mary bore sweet Jesus Christ
To do poor sinners good

4. The holly bears a prickle
As sharp as any thorn
And Mary bore sweet Jesus Christ
On Christmas day in the morn

5. The holly bears a bark
As bitter as the gall
And Mary bore sweet Jesus Christ
For to redeem us all

6. The holly and the ivy
Now both are full well grown
Of all trees that are in the wood
The holly bears the crown

In the bleak mid - win - ter, fros - ty wind made moan,
earth stood hard as i - ron, wa - ter like a stone.
Snow had fal - len, snow on snow, snow on snow,
in the bleak mid - win - ter, lo - ng a - go.

In the Bleak Midwinter

1. In the bleak midwinter, frosty wind made moan
Earth stood hard as iron, water like a stone
Snow had fallen, snow on snow, snow on snow
In the bleak midwinter, long ago

2. Our God, heaven cannot hold Him, nor earth sustain
Heaven and earth shall flee away when He comes to reign
In the bleak midwinter a stable place sufficed
The Lord God Almighty, Jesus Christ

3. Enough for Him, whom cherubim, worship night and day
Breastful of milk, and a mangerful of hay
Enough for Him, whom angels fall before
The ox and ass and camel which adore

4. Angels and archangels may have gathered there
Cherubim and seraphim thronged the air
But His mother only, in her maiden bliss
Worshipped the beloved with a kiss

5. What can I give Him, poor as I am?
If I were a shepherd, I would bring a lamb
If I were a wise man, I would do my part
Yet what I can I give Him: give my heart

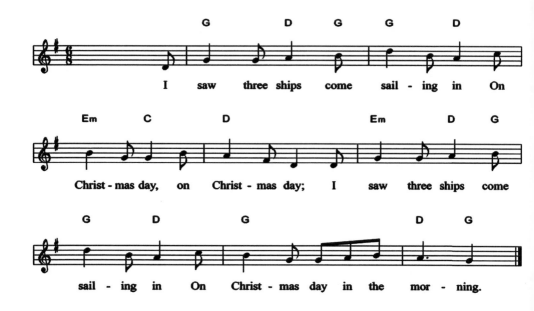

I saw three ships come sail - ing in On

Christ - mas day, on Christ - mas day; I saw three ships come

sail - ing in On Christ - mas day in the mor - ning.

I Saw Three Ships

1. I saw three ships come sailing in
On Christmas day, on Christmas day
I saw three ships come sailing in
On Christmas day in the morning

2. And what was in those ships all three
On Christmas day, on Christmas day?
And what was in those ships all three
On Christmas day in the morning?

3. Our Saviour Christ and His lady
On Christmas day, on Christmas day
Our Saviour Christ and His lady
On Christmas day in the morning

4. Pray whither sailed those ships all three
On Christmas day, on Christmas day?
Pray whither sailed those ships all three
On Christmas day in the morning?

5. O they sailed into Bethlehem
On Christmas day, on Christmas day
O they sailed into Bethlehem
On Christmas day in the morning

6. And all the bells on earth shall ring
On Christmas day, on Christmas day
And all the bells on earth shall ring
On Christmas day in the morning

7. And all the angels in heav'n shall sing
On Christmas day, on Christmas day
And all the angels in heav'n shall sing
On Christmas day in the morning

8. And all the souls on earth shall sing
On Christmas day, on Christmas day
And all the souls on earth shall sing
On Christmas day in the morning

9. Then let us all rejoice amain
On Christmas day, on Christmas day
Then let us rejoice amain
On Christmas day in the morning

It came up-on the mid-night clear, that glor-ious song of old, from an-gels ben-ding near the earth to touch their harps of gold: "Peace on the earth, good will to men, from heav'n's all-gra-cious King." The world in so-lemn still-ness lay to hear the an-gels sing.

It Came upon the Midnight Clear

1. It came upon the midnight clear
That glorious song of old
From angels bending near the earth
To touch their harps of gold
Peace on the earth, good will to men
From heaven's all gracious King
The world in solemn stillness lay
To hear the angels sing

2. Still through the cloven skies they come
With peaceful wings unfurled
And still their heavenly music floats
O'er all the weary world
Above its sad and lowly plains
They bend on hovering wing
And ever o'er its Babel sounds
The blessed angels sing

3. O ye, beneath life's crushing load
Whose forms are bending low
Who toil along the climbing way
With painful steps and slow
Look now, for glad and golden hours
Come swiftly on the wing
O rest beside the weary road
And hear the angels sing

4. For lo! the days are hastening on
By prophet-bards foretold
When with the ever circling years
Comes round the age of gold
When peace shall over all the earth
Its ancient splendors fling
And the whole world send back the song
Which now the angels sing

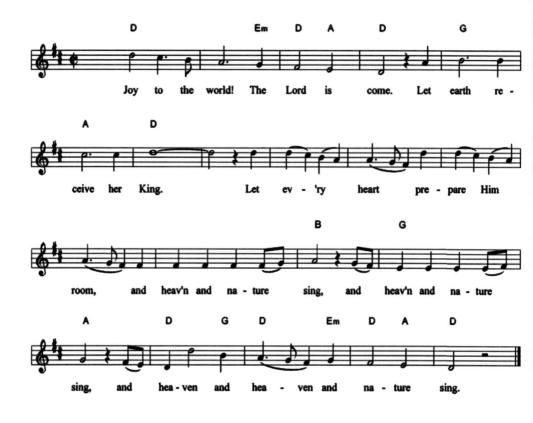

Joy to the world! The Lord is come. Let earth re-
ceive her King. Let ev-'ry heart pre-pare Him
room, and heav'n and na-ture sing, and heav'n and na-ture
sing, and hea-ven and hea-ven and na-ture sing.

Joy to the World

1. Joy to the world, the Lord is come!
Let earth receive her King
Let every heart prepare Him room
And heaven and nature sing
And heaven and nature sing
And heaven, and heaven, and nature sing

2. Joy to the earth, the Saviour reigns!
Let men their songs employ
While fields and floods, rocks, hills and plains
Repeat the sounding joy
Repeat the sounding joy
Repeat, repeat, the sounding joy

3. No more let sins and sorrows grow
Nor thorns infest the ground
He comes to make His blessings flow
Far as the curse is found
Far as the curse is found
Far as, far as, the curse is found

4. He rules the world with truth and grace
And makes the nations prove
The glories of His righteousness
And wonders of His love
And wonders of His love
And wonders, wonders, of His love

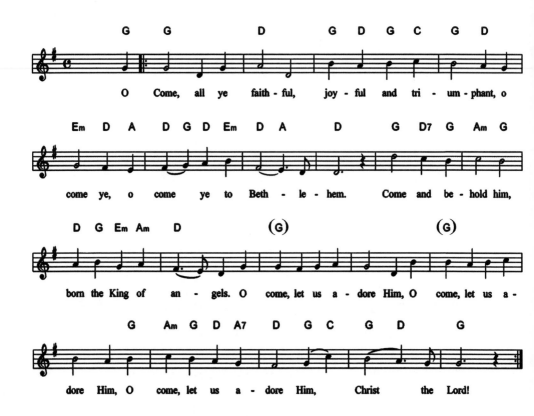

O Come, All Ye Faithful

O come, all ye faithful, joyful and triumphant
O come ye, O come ye, to Bethlehem
Come and behold Him, born the King of angels
O come, let us adore Him
O come, let us adore Him
O come, let us adore Him
Christ the Lord

Sing, choirs of angels, sing in exultation
O sing, all ye citizens of heaven above
Glory to God, all glory in the highest
O come, let us adore Him
O come, let us adore Him
O come, let us adore Him
Christ the Lord

Yea, Lord, we greet Thee, born this happy morning
Jesus, to Thee be glory given
Word of the Father, now in flesh appearing
O come, let us adore Him
O come, let us adore Him
O come, let us adore Him
Christ the Lord

O come, O come, Em - man - u - el, and ran - som cap - tive
Is - - - ra - el that mourns in lone - ly ex - ile
here un - til the Son of God ap - pear. Re -
joice! Re - joice! Em - man - u - el shall come to thee, O Is - ra - el!

O Come, O Come Emmanuel

1. O come, O come Emmanuel
And ransom captive Israel
That mourns in lonely exile here
Until the Son of God appear
Rejoice! Rejoice! Emmanuel
Shall come to thee, O Israel

2. O come, Thou Rod of Jesse, free
Thine own from Satan's tyranny
From depths of Hell Thy people save
And give them victory o'er the grave

3. O come, Thou Day-Spring, come and cheer
Our spirits by Thine advent here
Disperse the gloomy clouds of night
And death's dark shadows put to flight

4. O come, Thou Key of David, come
And open wide our heavenly home
Make safe the way that leads on high
And close the path to misery

5. O come, O come, Thou Lord of might
Who to Thy tribes, on Sinai's height
In ancient times did'st give the law
In cloud, and majesty and awe

| C | F | B♭ | F | Gm | F | Dm | | C | Dm | Gm | F/A | Gm/B♭ | C7 | F | C |

O lit - tle town of Beth - le - hem, how still we see thee lie! A -

| F | B♭ | F | Gm | F | Dm | | C | Dm | Gm | F/A | Gm/B♭ | C7 | F | Dm |

bove thy deep and dream - less sleep the si - lent stars go by. Yet

| Am | C7 | | F | Dm | C | F/A | F | Gm/B♭ | Dm | C | C7 |

in thy dark streets shi - - - neth the ev - er - las - ting Light; The

| F | B♭ | F/A | Gm | F | Dm | C | Dm | Gm | F/A | Csus4 | C7 | F |

hopes and fears of all the years are met in thee to - night.

O Little Town of Bethlehem

1. O little town of Bethlehem, how still we see thee lie
Above thy deep and dreamless sleep the silent stars go by
Yet in thy dark streets shineth the everlasting Light
The hopes and fears of all the years
Are met in thee tonight

2. For Christ is born of Mary, and gathered all above
While mortals sleep, the angels keep their watch of wondering love
O morning stars together, proclaim the holy birth
And praises sing to God the King
And peace to men on earth

3. How silently, how silently, the wondrous Gift is giv'n
So God imparts to human hearts the blessings of His heav'n
No ear may hear His coming, but in this world of sin
Where meek souls will receive Him still
The dear Christ enters in

4. Where children pure and happy pray to the blessed Child
Where misery cries out to Thee, Son of the mother mild
Where charity stands watching and faith holds wide the door
The dark night wakes, the glory breaks
And Christmas comes once more

5. O holy Child of Bethlehem, descend to us, we pray
Cast out our sin, and enter in, be born in us today
We hear the Christmas angels the great glad tidings tell
O come to us, abide with us
Our Lord Emmanuel

Si - lent night, ho - ly night, all is calm, all is bright
round yon vir - gin moth-er and child. Ho - ly in - fant so ten - der and mild,
sleep in heav - en - ly peace, sleep in heav - en - ly peace.

Silent Night

Silent night, holy night
All is calm, all is bright
Round yon Virgin Mother and Child
Holy Infant so tender and mild
Sleep in heavenly peace
Sleep in heavenly peace

Silent night, holy night!
Shepherds quake at the sight
Glories stream from heaven afar
Heavenly hosts sing Alleluia!
Christ, the Saviour is born
Christ, the Saviour is born

Silent night, holy night
Son of God, love's pure light
Radiant beams from Thy holy face
With the dawn of redeeming grace
Jesus, Lord, at Thy birth
Jesus, Lord, at Thy birth

We three kings of O - ri - ent are bear - ing gifts we tra - verse a -
far. Field and foun-tain, moor and moun - tain, fol - low - ing yon - der star.
O star of won - der, star of night, star with roy - al beau - ty bright,
west - ward lead - ing, still pro - ceed - ing, guide us to thy per - fect light.

We Three Kings of Orient Are

1. We three kings of Orient are
Bearing gifts we traverse afar
Field and fountain, moor and mountain
Following yonder star
O Star of wonder, star of night
Star with royal beauty bright
Westward leading, still proceeding
Guide us to Thy perfect light

2. Born a King on Bethlehem's plain
Gold I bring to crown Him again
King forever, ceasing never
Over us all to rein

3. Frankincense to offer have I
Incense owns a Deity nigh
Pray'r and praising, all men raising
Worship Him, God most high

4. Myrrh is mine, its bitter perfume
Breathes of life of gathering gloom
Sorrowing, sighing, bleeding, dying
Sealed in the stone-cold tomb

5. Glorious now behold Him arise
King and God and Sacrifice
Alleluia, Alleluia
Earth to heav'n replies

We Wish You a Merry Christmas

We wish you a Merry Christmas
We wish you a Merry Christmas
We wish you a Merry Christmas
And a Happy New Year
Good tidings we bring to you and your kin
Good tidings for Christmas
And a Happy New Year

Oh, bring us a figgy pudding
Oh, bring us a figgy pudding
Oh, bring us a figgy pudding
And a cup of good cheer
We won't go until we get some
We won't go until we get some
We won't go until we get some
So bring some out here

We wish you a Merry Christmas
We wish you a Merry Christmas
We wish you a Merry Christmas
And a Happy New Year

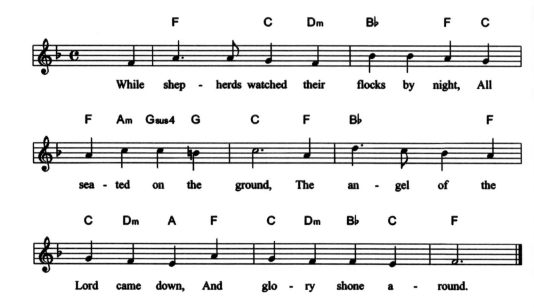

While shep - herds watched their flocks by night, All sea - ted on the ground, The an - gel of the Lord came down, And glo - ry shone a - round.

While Shepherds Watched Their Flocks

1. While shepherds watched their flocks by night
All seated on the ground
The angel of the Lord came down
And glory shone around

2. Fear not, said he, for mighty dread
Had seized their troubled minds
Glad tidings of great joy I bring
To you and all mankind

3. To you in David's town this day
Is born of David's line
A Saviour who is Christ the Lord
And this shall be the sign

4. The heavenly Babe you there shall find
To human view displayed
All meanly wrapped in swathing bands
And in a manger laid

5. Thus spake the seraph, and forthwith
Appeared a shining throng
Of angels praising God, who thus
Addressed their joyful song

6. All glory be to God on high
And to the earth be peace
Goodwill henceforth from heaven to men
Begin and never cease

Epiphany Carols.

mf As with glad-ness men of old Did the guid-ing Star be-hold; cr As with joy they hailed its light, Lead-ing on-ward, beaming bright;

p So, most grac-ious LORD, may we cr E-ver-more be led to Thee.

mf As with joyful steps they sped,
dim SAVIOUR, to Thy lowly bed,
p There to bend the knee before
Him Whom heaven and earth adore;
So may we with willing feet
cr Ever seek Thy mercy-seat.

mf As they offered gifts most rare
At Thy cradle rude and bare;
So may we with holy joy,
Pure and free from sin's alloy,
All our costliest treasures bring,
cr CHRIST, to Thee, our heavenly KING.

mf Holy JESUS! every day
Keep us in the narrow way;
And, when earthly things are past,
Bring our ransomed souls at last
Where they need no star to guide,
cr Where no clouds Thy glory hide.

mf In the heavenly country bright
Need they no created light;
Thou its Light, its Joy, its Crown,
Thou its Sun which goes not down;
ff There for ever may we sing
cr Alleluias to our KING.

Carols for Use in Church, 1894

Away in a manger.

(CRADLE CAROL.)

J. E. Spilman.

1. A-way in a man-ger, No crib for His bed, The lit-tle Lord Je-sus Lay down His sweet head: The stars in the heav-ens Look'd down where He lay, The lit-tle Lord Je-sus A-sleep in the hay. The cat-tle are low-ing, The poor ba-by wakes, But lit-tle Lord Je-sus No cry-ing He makes; I love Thee, Lord Je-sus, Look down from the sky, And stay by my cra-dle To watch lull-a-by.

2. Be near me, Lord Je-sus, I ask Thee to stay Close by me' for ev-er And love me, I pray: Bless all the dear chil-dren In Thy ten-der care, And take us to heav-en To live with Thee there. A-way in a man-ger, No crib for His bed, The lit-tle Lord Je-sus Lay down His sweet head; The stars in the heav-ens Look'd down where He lay, The lit-tle Lord Je-sus, A-sleep in the hay.

DECK THE HALL WITH HOLLY.

1. Deck the hall with boughs of hol - ly,
2. See the blaz - ing yule be - fore us,
Fast a - way the old year pass - es,
Fa la la la la la la la la,

'Tis the sea-son to be jol - ly,
Strike the harp and join the chorus,
Hail the new, ye lads and lasses,
Fa la la la la la la la la.
Don we now our
Fol - low me in
Sing we joy - ous

gay ap par - el, Troll the ancient Christmas car - ol,
mer - ry measure, While I tell of Christmas treasure,
all to-geth - er, Heedless of the wind and weather,
Fa la la la la la la la la.

VIII. DING DONG! MERRILY ON HIGH

Words by G. R. W. Tune, *Branle de l'Official*, from Thoinot Arbeau's *Orchésographie*, (1588), harmonized by C. W.

1. Ding dong! mer-ri-ly on high in heav'n the bells are ring - ing:
   Ding dong! ver-i-ly the sky is riv'n with An-gel sing - ing.

2. E'en so here be-low, be - low, let stee-ple bells be swung - en,
   And i - o, i - o, i - o, by priest and peo - ple sung - en.

3. Pray you, du-ti-ful-ly prime your Mat - in chime, ye ring - ers;
   May you beau-ti-ful-ly rime your Eve - time Song, ye sing - ers:

Glo - - - - - - - - ri-a, Ho - san - na in ex - cel - sis!

The Cambridge Carol-Book, Being Fifty-Two Songs
For Christmas, Easter, And Other Seasons, 1924

43

Christmas-tide, Its History, Festivities and Carols,
With Their Music, 1852

God rest you, merry Gentlemen.

God rest you, mer - ry gen - tle - men, Let noth-ing you dis - may, Re -

- mem-ber Christ our Sa - vi-our Was born on Christmas Day ; To save us all from

ff Chorus.

Satan's pow'r When we were gone a-stray ; O ti - dings of com - fort and

joy, com - fort and joy, O ti - dings of com - fort and joy.

Christmas Carols - New and Old, First Series, circa 1860

Good King Wenceslas.

CHRISTMAS.

Words by J. M. Neale.   Traditional.

2

Ten.* Solo. "Hither, page, and stand by me,
    If thou know'st it, telling,
Yonder peasant, who is he?
    Where and what his dwelling?"

Treb. Solo. "Sire, he lives a good league hence,
    Underneath the mountain;
Right against the forest fence,
    By Saint Agnes' fountain."

3

Ten. Solo. "Bring me flesh, and bring me wine,
    Bring me pine-logs hither;
Thou and I will see him dine,
    When we bear them thither."

Cho. Page and monarch forth they went,
    Forth they went together;
Through the rude wind's wild lament;
    And the bitter weather.

4

Treb. Solo. "Sire, the night is darker now,
    And the wind blows stronger;
Fails my heart, I know not how,
    I can go no longer."

Ten. Solo. "Mark my footsteps, my good page;
    Tread thou in them boldly:
Thou shalt find the winter's rage
    Freeze thy blood less coldly."

5

Cho. In his master's steps he trod,
    Where the snow lay dinted;
Heat was in the very sod
    Which the saint had printed.
Therefore, Christian men, be sure,
    Wealth or rank possessing,
Ye who now will bless the poor,
    Shall yourselves find blessing.

* All the verses may be sung in chorus if preferred.

Carols Old and Carols New, 1916

Hark! the herald angels sing.

Words by *Rev. C. Wesley.*

Mendelssohn.

Carols Old and Carols New, 1916

The Holly and the Ivy.

Words from an early
18th Century BROADSIDE.

Old French melody
traditionally sung to the words.

The Cornish Song Book, 1929

48

In the bleak midwinter.

CHRISTMAS.

Carol 652.

Words by *C. G. Rossetti.*

Thomas B. Strong.

Slow. VERSE 1.

1. In the bleak mid - win - ter Fros - ty wind made moan, Earth stood hard as i - ron, Wa - ter like a stone. Snow had fall - en, snow on snow, Snow on snow, In the bleak . mid - win - ter, Long a - go.

VERSE 2.

2. Our God, hea - ven can - not hold Him, Nor earth sus - tain; Heav'n and earth shall flee a - way When He comes to reign; In the bleak mid - win - - ter A sta - ble - place suf - ficed The . Lord God Al - migh - ty Je - sus Christ.

VERSE 3

3. E - nough for Him, whom Che - ru - bim Wor - ship night and

Carols Old and Carols New, 1916

I SAW THREE SHIPS.

Christmas-tide, Its History,
Festivities and Carols, With Their Music, 1852

It Came Upon the Midnight Clear

Public Domain Score

ANTIOCH

Ascribed to G. F. Handel, 1742, by L. Mason, 1830.

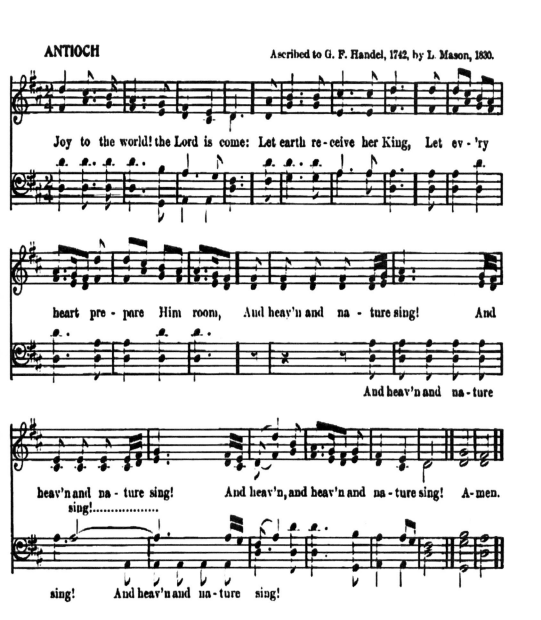

Joy to the world! the Lord is come: Let earth re-ceive her King, Let ev-'ry

heart pre-pare Him room, And heav'n and na-ture sing! And

And heav'n and na-ture

heav'n and na-ture sing! And heav'n, and heav'n and na-ture sing! A-men.

sing!..................

sing! And heav'n and na-ture sing!

Hymns of the Kingdom of God, 1910

Christmas.

ADESTE FIDELES.

1. O come, all ye faith-ful, Joy-ful and tri-um-phant, O come ye, O come ye to Beth-le-hem: Come and be-hold Him King of all the an-gels! O come, let us a-dore Him, O come, let us a-dore Him, O come, let us a-dore Him, Christ the Lord.

The Wartburg Hymnal, 1918

Veni, veni, Emmanuel!

Melody from a French Miffal.
Harmonized by H. R. Schroeder.

*Great Hymns of the Church Compiled by
the Late Right Reverend John Freeman Young, 1887*

FOREST GREEN. (D.C. M. Words irreg.)

In moderate time ♩ = 80.

English Traditional Melody.

Org.

Suitable till Candlemas.

Bp. Phillips Brooks, 1835-93.

Stille Nacht! heilige Nacht!

Si - lent night! Ho - ly night! All is calm, all is bright,

Round yon Vir - gin Mother and Child! Ho - ly In-fant, so ten-der and mild,

Sleep in heav - en - ly peace, Sleep in heav - en - ly peace.

Great Hymns of the Church, 1887

Carols, Hymns and Songs, 1863

58

WE WISH YOU A MERRY CHRISTMAS

Public Domain Score

WHILE SHEPHERDS WATCHED THEIR FLOCKS.

WINCHESTER OLD.

Est's *Psalmes*, 1592.